CODE OF PRACTICE ON
FOOD HYGIENE INSPECTIONS

(Code of Practice No 9 Revised)

1 This new version of Code No 9 contains changes which include advice on enforcement of the Food Safety (General Food Hygiene) Regulations 1995. These Regulations and this new version of the Code come into force from 15 September 1995.

2 Certain guidance on the qualifications of inspectors does not come into force until 1 April 2000—see paragraph 41 and its footnote.

The sections in **bold type** are a Code of Practice issued under section 40 of the Food Safety Act 1990 which food authorities must have regard to. The remaining text is for information only.

A.   Introduction

1   This Code of Practice gives guidance to food authorities on the frequency and nature of inspections carried out to assess the hygiene of premises and the public health protection aspects of food law. *Annex 1* to this Code contains advice on a scheme to determine the minimum frequency of inspection based on an evaluation of the potential risk. This Code applies unless more specific guidelines on inspections are laid down under other food legislation, for example *Code of Practice No 15: Enforcement of the Food Safety (Fishery Products) Regulations 1992.*

2   The Code also gives guidance to Food Authorities on the approach to the enforcement of the Food Safety (General Food Hygiene) Regulations 1995. Advice on these Regulations is specifically identified in the text.

3   A separate Code of Practice gives guidance on food standards inspections *(Code of Practice No 8)*. Both these Codes should be read in conjunction with *Code of Practice No 3: Inspection Procedures—General*, which gives a definition of the term "inspection" and guidance on whether to give notice of inspection visits, the co-ordination of inspection visits, visits to premises outside the food authority's area and post inspection procedures.

4   *Annex 2* to this Code explains the application of the Food Safety Act to primary producers of food and food sources, such as farmers and growers.

1

B. Purpose of Food Hygiene Inspections

5   **Food hygiene inspections have two main purposes:**

   i.   **First, authorised officers should seek to identify risks arising from the activities carried on and the effectiveness of food businesses' own assessment of hazards and control of risks.** This hazard analysis approach shifts the emphasis from final product testing and consideration of the structure and layout of premises to raw materials and process control.

   Many businesses have developed their own systems of hazard analysis. This Code recognises the relevance of effective hazard analysis both in carrying out the inspection and in determining the frequency of inspections. The Food Safety (General Food Hygiene) Regulations 1995 and other food hygiene and processing regulations make clear that the primary responsibility for identifying food hazards and controlling risks rests with food businesses.

   ii.   **Second, they should identify contraventions of the Food Safety Act 1990 and food hygiene and processing regulations and seek to have them corrected.**

   In considering enforcement action, food authorities should have regard to risks arising from contraventions, the nature of the food business, and the nature and type of food handled. Food authorities should also have regard to *Code of Practice No 2 on Legal Matters* and *Code of Practice No 5 on the Use of Improvement Notices* when considering enforcement action.

6   **Authorised officers should be prepared to offer advice where this is appropriate or is requested and encourage food businesses to adopt good food hygiene practice, particularly that set out in relevant UK or EC Industry Guides to Good Hygiene Practice.**[1]

C. Official Control of Foodstuffs Directive (89/397/EEC)

7   This Directive is one of the key directives adopted by the European Community in order to bring about a single market

---

[1] References to "UK Industry Guides to Good Hygiene Practice" in this Code mean Guides which are recognized by UK Government as Guides which are presumed to comply with the Food Safety (General Food Hygiene) Regulations 1995. "EC Industry Guides" are those recognized by the European Community as Guides presumed to comply with Article 3 of the EC Food Hygiene Directive.

in foodstuffs. One of its aims is to ensure that Member States can have confidence in each others' food law enforcement arrangements. The basic principle is that food should be inspected primarily at the point of production so that there is no need for regular border controls when food moves between Member States.

D. Products Intended for Sale Outside the United Kingdom

8   Under the Official Control of Foodstuffs Directive, Member States must "ensure that products intended for consignment to another Member State are inspected with the same care as those intended for marketing on their own territory", and Member States may "not exclude a product from appropriate control on the grounds that it is intended for export outside the Community".

9   **Authorised officers should inspect products intended for sale anywhere within the European Community with the same care as they inspect products intended for sale in the United Kingdom. When inspecting manufacturing premises they should check that products intended for sale within the EC are manufactured in accordance with United Kingdom legislation.** Products for trade with other EC Member States may in theory comply with lesser requirements in other Members States' legislation, in the few instances where requirements have yet to be harmonised by the EC. This should be an increasingly rare situation as food hygiene requirements are harmonised within the EC Single Market.

10   **Authorised officers should not exclude products from inspection on the grounds that they are intended for export outside the Community.**

E. Priority Planning and Programme of Inspections

11   Under the Official Control of Foodstuffs Directive, Member States have to draw up programmes for inspections of food premises and ensure that inspections are carried out "regularly" (although the Directive does not define what is meant by "regularly").

12   **Each food authority with responsibility for food hygiene must adopt a programme for food hygiene inspections and, as far as practicable, ensure that inspection visits are carried out in accordance with that programme. Food authorities should observe the minimum inspection frequencies set out in paragraph 17.**

13　Some food premises and businesses will present a higher risk to the consumer than others. An effective inspection programme should recognise that the frequency of the inspection will vary according to the type of food business and the nature of the food, the degree of handling and the size of the business. Those premises posing potentially a higher risk should be inspected more frequently than those premises with a lower risk.

14　Food authorities should adopt a scheme of priority classification of food premises in their area using either the inspection rating scheme set out in *Annex 1*, or by adopting a scheme which operates to similar principles and results in at least the same minimum inspection frequencies.

15　Any scheme used should take account of management practices and past compliance with the legislation in determining *likely future risk*. It is not sufficient for food authorities to operate an inspection rating scheme based solely on the type of premises. Well-run businesses with good comprehensive internal control systems, (and possibly their own effective inspection programme) will not need to be inspected with the same frequency as similar businesses which do not have such management control systems.

16　Premises which are used occasionally for a food business need not be subject to the same frequency of inspection as a similar business operating on a more regular basis. The inspection rating scheme recognises that premises used infrequently, particularly by voluntary and charitable groups, generally pose a lower risk.

Frequency of Inspection

17　Once the food authority has determined the relative extent of risk, premises should be inspected within the following minimum frequencies:—

Category	Minimum Frequency of Inspection
A	(at least) every 6 months
B	(at least) every year
C	(at least) every 18 months
D	(at least) every 2 years
E	(at least) every 3 years
F	(at least) every 5 years

18　Food authorities should regard the inspection frequencies set out in paragraph 17 as the minimum and may provide for more frequent inspections where they consider this appropriate.

19   Where requested, the food authority should advise the proprietor or representative of the inspection rating allocated to the business and be prepared to discuss the scoring applied. The food authority should emphasise that the inspection rating is a guide to the minimum frequency of inspection.

High Risk Activities

20   The inspection rating scheme will ensure that food authorities have special regard to food businesses which are involved in methods of preparation including processing, cooking and packaging of food which present particular risks.

Follow-up visits

21   If contraventions of food hygiene or processing regulations are found during the programmed inspection, the food authority should arrange to carry out a further visit to the business, if necessary. The timing of this visit will be determined by the action taken by the food authority as a result of the original inspection.

Combined Visits

22   Combining a food hygiene inspection with another visit to the same premises can help make effective use of food authority resources and minimise disruption to businesses. Wherever it is practicable and appropriate to do so, a food hygiene inspection should be combined with:

— a food standards inspection where the officer is responsible for the enforcement of both food hygiene and food standards matters;

— an inspection carried out under other legislation; and/or

— another visit for food hygiene purposes (for example, to investigate a complaint or a problem which has arisen further down the food chain or to respond to a request for advice).

F.   The Inspection

23   Legal requirements in relation to hazard analysis systems in "Vertical" product-specific food hygiene regulations and in

the Food Safety (General Food Hygiene) Regulations 1995 differ. This section contains advice on how the approach to inspection will be affected by the existence of satisfactory hazard analysis systems in food businesses, irrespective of whether there is a legal requirement on the business for such a system.

24   Inspections should:

— include a preliminary assessment of the food safety hazards associated with the business and

— look at whether the business has a satisfactory system (a "hazard analysis system") for assessing food hazards and controlling risks. The approach to inspections should be changed significantly where there is such a system in place, as described in paragraphs 27 to 29.

For a hazard analysis system to be regarded as satisfactory, this should include a commitment to proper management controls. A well documented hazard analysis system by itself may be of little benefit without a commitment to proper use of that hazard analysis. References in this Code to "hazard analysis systems" should be read as including both the identification and implementation of appropriate measures of control.

25   Before commencing the inspection the officer should ensure that the proprietor or his representative is aware of the purpose of the inspection. Authorised officers should make available copies of the leaflet "Food Law Inspections and your Business".

26   Hazard analysis systems and the ways in which businesses control risks will vary greatly, depending on the type of business, the size of operation, the food safety hazards associated with that operation, and risks to the consumer. (See Section K on general enforcement of hazard analysis requirements and Section L on hazard analysis requirements arising from the Food Safety (General Food Hygiene) Regulations 1995.)

27   An inspection should normally include a discussion with the proprietor or representative on matters relating to hygiene systems and procedures. An examination of documentation (where appropriate), particularly that related to monitoring of critical control points may be helpful in the discussion. A vital part of this discussion will cover the business's own management controls. Where:

— there are satisfactory management controls as part of a well thought out hazard analysis system, and

— the authorised officer has confidence in the management of the business on the basis of previous inspections,

the consideration of hazard analysis and controls should be a significant part of the inspection and may take up a major part of the time involved. A main purpose of subsequent visual or physical examination should be to confirm that critical points have been correctly identified and that controls are in place.

28   The adequacy or otherwise of any hygiene system/records should be assessed. Any unforeseen potential hazard identified through this assessment should be discussed with the proprietor or representative during or at the conclusion of the visit and confirmed in writing thereafter (see paragraphs 32 and 33).

29   Where a satisfactory hazard analysis system is not in place, the authorised officer may need to carry out a fuller visual and physical examination of the premises. The officer should have special regard to the hazards associated with the business, to identify those areas of the processing, distribution, handling, storage and display of food which require closer scrutiny. This will enable the officer to focus the inspection on the areas of greatest potential concern.

30   When exercising their power to inspect process records and other trade secrets, authorised officers should bear in mind that it is an offence to disclose any trade secret (such as a secret manufacturing process) unless the disclosure is made in the performance of the authorised officer's duty.

Unit Inspection

31   Authorities may wish to consider whether "unit inspection" would be a useful concept for them to include in their priority system. Unitisation of large premises into sub-divisions allows each sub-division or unit to be separately assessed and separately inspected. Such a system might be particularly useful where food hygiene inspection of a unit, for example a restaurant in a department store, is likely to be needed more frequently than for the rest of the premises.

Reports

32   On completion of the inspection the officer should discuss with the proprietor or representative a summary of the matters which, in the opinion of the officer, breach the requirements of the Act or regulations and any advice on good food hygiene practice he may wish to give.

33   Authorised officers should report back in writing after every programmed inspection and, where appropriate, after other inspections. Reports should include all the items covered in the sample report form at *Annex 3*.

Clothing and Equipment

34   Food authorities should provide officers who carry out inspections with the necessary clean protective clothing including head gear as appropriate. Officers should ensure that they wear protective clothing and adhere to any reasonable food safety precautions which are required by the company or organisation under inspection. Where the company or organisation provides its own appropriate protective clothing, this should be worn by the officer.

35   Food authorities should provide officers with all of the equipment necessary to carry out a full and detailed inspection, including appropriate thermometers or other temperature monitoring equipment. Where monitoring equipment is used the officer should take steps to prevent cross-contamination. In England and Wales, see *Code of Practice No 10: Enforcement of the Temperature Control Requirements of Food Hygiene Regulations.*

Timing of Inspections

36   Some food businesses only operate in the early hours of the morning, late at night or at weekends. An effective inspection programme will need to recognise that such food businesses should be visited outside normal food authority hours of work.

G.   Qualifications of Inspectors

37   Food authorities with responsibility for food hygiene should appoint at least one environmental health officer with specialist responsibility for food hygiene and food safety matters. Food authorities may establish a team of officers consisting of environmental health officers, together with

suitably qualified food technologists, technicians or assistants with responsibility for such matters.

38 Inspections of food premises should only be undertaken by officers who are suitably qualified and experienced and who have a knowledge of:

— relevant regulations;

— Codes of Practice issued under section 40 of the Food Safety Act;

— UK or EC Industry Guides; and

— relevant advice issued by Central Government Departments or by LACOTS.

Officers may be assisted in such inspections by those who are not so qualified.

39 Premises which fall within risk categories A and B according to the inspection rating scheme in *Annex 1*, those of all food manufacturers and processors classified as substantial under paragraph 2.8 of *Annex 1*, and premises which are approved or require approval under product-specific food hygiene regulations should be inspected only by environmental health officers, official veterinary surgeons (where appropriate), or officers holding one of the following qualifications:

— Higher Certificate in Food Premises Inspection, issued by one of the following:

The Environmental Health Officers' Registration Board (EHORB), the Scottish Food Safety Officers' Registration Board (SFSORB), or the Institute of Food Science and Technology (IFST)

The Certificate would not be issued until the requirements of paragraph 43 have been satisfied.

40 Premises may change risk category between inspections, eg, a premises formerly in category C may appear on inspection to fall into category B. Except for food manufacturers and processors classified as substantial under paragraph 2.8 of *Annex 1*, and premises which require approval under product-specific food hygiene regulations, the inspection *may* be completed for that occasion only, even if carried out by an officer possessing only the qualifications set out in paragraph 41. But food authorities should ensure that the outcome of the inspection and any action proposed are

validated by an officer holding the qualifications in paragraph 39[2,3]

41   All other premises must be inspected by officers who have either one of the qualifications set out in paragraph 39, or an Ordinary Certificate in Food Premises Inspection issued by one of the following:[4]

The Environmental Health Officers' Registration Board (EHORB), the Scottish Food Safety Officers' Registration Board (SFSORB), or the Institute of Food Science and Technology (IFST).

42   Before authorising an officer to inspect any premises, the food authority should be satisfied that the officer is competent to do so, is qualified as set out above and possesses the necessary experience to undertake the duty. Food authorities should give particular attention to the need for authorised officers to receive appropriate training in hazard analysis systems.

43   All officers other than environmental health officers and official veterinary surgeons will require a period of structured practical training with a food enforcement authority of not less than 6 months.

H.   Monitoring of the Quality of Inspections

44   Food authorities should maintain a documented management system to monitor the quality and nature of inspections undertaken by their officers to ensure, so far as practicable, that inspections are carried out to a uniform standard. The management monitoring system should also ensure that the interpretation and action taken by officers following an inspection is consistent within that authority. Food authorities should consider undertaking joint exercises with adjoining authorities to assess their consistency of interpretation and approach.

---

[2] Paragraphs 39 and 40 apply from 15 September 1995 in England and Wales and from 15 September 1996 in Scotland.

[3] Existing officers who marginally fail the assessment for the Higher Certificate in food premises inspection and are referred by the Assessment Body may continue to inspect food premises falling within the definition of paragraph 39 for a further period of 12 months from the date of their referral. Food authorities should ensure that the outcome of the inspection and any action proposed are confirmed by an officer holding the qualifications in paragraph 39.

[4] Until 31 March 2000, officers who are suitably experienced and competent but who do not hold such qualifications may undertake inspections covered in this paragraph.

I. Co-ordination of Advice and Enforcement

45   The co-ordination of food authority advice and enforcement is essential to ensure uniformity of treatment and consistency in dealing with food businesses who have more than one branch or unit and these are situated in different food authority areas.

46   **Food authorities should, therefore, be guided by LACOTS' home authority principle in determining which food authority should take lead (home authority) responsibility for giving advice to food businesses which have more than one branch or unit situated in different food authority areas on matters relating to food hygiene legislation.**

47   **Food authorities considering giving detailed advice or taking enforcement action in relation to food businesses which have branches or units situated in other food authority areas should consider whether they need to contact the home authority before doing so.** This may be necessary, for example, where the advice or enforcement action relates to centrally agreed policies or procedures of a food business. It would not be necessary, however, where such action relates to matters of an exclusively local nature.

48   **Food authorities acting as home authority should recognise that whilst they will be providing advice to a particular food business whose decision making base is located in their area, there will be other similar food businesses in the same sector of the industry who have other food authorities acting as home authority, eg the different national chains of pizza houses. Groups of home authorities serving food businesses trading in the same sector of the industry should consider the benefits of regular liaison. LACOTS is willing to assist home authorities to develop these liaison arrangements.**

J. Action to be Taken when Breaches of Regulations are Identified

49   An authorised officer has a range of options available when breaches of hygiene or processing regulations are identified during an inspection. Advice on the enforcement action possible is included in *Code of Practice No 5: The Use of Improvement Notices* and *Code of Practice No 6: Prohibition Procedures*. Informal advice or a letter should be used if such an approach is likely to be as effective as statutory means of enforcement.

50   An authorised officer may wish to offer informal written advice when poor hygiene practices are identified which do

not constitute a breach of regulations or where industry recommended codes of practice have not been followed. This information may be helpful to the proprietor and may be a relevant record for the authority in any assessment of the diligence exercised by the proprietor.

51 Where food authorities provide advice on food hygiene, they should ensure that there is a clear distinction between matters which are necessary to meet statutory requirements and those which are recommended as good hygiene practice. Food authorities should also ensure that advice or interpretation of requirements contained in any word processed document or pre-printed letter, circular or advisory booklet, whether or not issued as part of an inspection, is accurate and reflects current practice.

52 The food authority should ensure, whenever possible, that any improvement notices, informal written advice or inspection report following an inspection are sent to the proprietor together.

53 In deciding what measures need to be taken to meet contraventions of hygiene or processing regulations, food authorities may refer to the advice and recommendations contained within national guidelines or industry codes of recommended practice. Food authorities should be aware that the Food Safety Act allows food businesses issued with an improvement notice to take other steps to comply with regulations as long as these achieve the same effect. Food authorities must give due consideration to any relevant UK or EC Industry Guides to Good Hygiene Practice when assessing compliance with the Food Safety (General Food Hygiene) Regulations 1995—see paragraph 80.

54 The food authority should have regard to any advice or opinion given by Central Government. Where no central government guidance has been issued, the food authority should have regard to any advice given by LACOTS. Where a food authority wishes to adopt an approach which is not consistent with that expressed by a national co-ordinating body they should first discuss their approach with that body.

55 Where issues of interpretation and inconsistency arise, authorised officers should discuss areas of difficulty with colleagues in other authorities. Whatever problems are encountered, food authorities should avoid taking a unilateral decision on interpretation without seeking the views of other authorities or of a national coordinating body. The appropriate local body for consultation would be the local food liaison group recognized by LACOTS.

K. Approach to Enforcement of Requirements Related to Hazard Analysis Systems and Food Hygiene Training

56   The following paragraphs give general advice on enforcement of these requirements. See Section L of this Code for specific advice on enforcement of the Food Safety (General Food Hygiene) Regulations 1995 and separate Codes for advice on "Vertical" product specific food hygiene Regulations.

57   **Food authorities should adopt a graduated approach to enforcement. As the first step towards securing compliance, the authorised officer should adopt an educative approach and discuss the requirements of the legislation relating to hazard analysis and training and supervision with the proprietor.** The aim should be to encourage the adoption of a preventive approach to food safety, even where there is no immediate risk to public health apparent at the time of inspection.

58   **In considering formal approaches to enforcement, food authorities should take account of whether there is also evidence of a significant breach of other food hygiene requirements. Clear breaches of requirements relating to hazard analysis systems and food hygiene training would normally be expected to lead to significant breaches of other food hygiene requirements.** The objective of a hazard analysis system, for example, should be to have effective food hygiene controls in place. Where effective controls are in place which achieve food safety and meet other food hygiene requirements, but a satisfactory hazard analysis system or food hygiene training are not in place, formal enforcement action will be based largely on a judgement of the effect of these breaches on the future safety of food within the business. Authorised officers should take particular care with formal enforcement action in these situations for low risk businesses. Care should also be taken to avoid an undue emphasis on documentation of hazard analysis systems.

59   **In the absence of any evidence which indicates a significant breach of other food hygiene requirements, food authorities may nevertheless consider a formal approach to enforcement where:**

— **the businesses involve high risk operations;**

— **the breaches of requirements relating to hazard analysis systems or those relating to training and/or supervision would be likely to lead to significant breaches of other food hygiene requirements, if not remedied; this might** apply, for example, where there has been a general failure to set up a hazard analysis system, but would not apply where there was a minor error in the analysis, or in the controls instituted, or a minor error of documentation; and

— the food business has failed to respond to an informal, educative approach.

60   Where food authorities find it necessary to adopt a formal approach to the enforcement of the regulations relating to the training and/or supervision of food handlers, they should not invite the business to participate in food hygiene training which is provided by the authority because of the potential conflict of interest.

L.   Enforcement of Requirements of the Food Safety (General Food Hygiene) Regulations 1995

i. Requirements for Hazard Analysis Systems

61   The ways in which businesses identify food hazards and identify and implement control and monitoring procedures at critical points will vary greatly, depending on the type of business, the size of operation, the food safety hazards associated with that operation, and risks to the consumer. In certain high risk businesses and operations, a formal, documented hazard analysis system based on specialist advice may be necessary to establish effective controls. Enforcement officers may therefore wish to encourage documented hazard analysis systems in such situations, although a documented system would not be an express legal requirement.

62   In other businesses, the hazard analysis should still follow a structured approach to identifying hazards and controlling risks, but could rely on generic advice on the hazards and necessary controls in such businesses, including advice in Industry Guides to Good Hygiene Practice. Levels of documentation, where this is appropriate, to record the critical control points identified and monitoring will vary according to the factors listed in paragraph 61.

63   Lower risk operations are unlikely to need formal, documented hazard analysis systems. The smaller span of control in smaller businesses is relevant in assessing risk and therefore in determining whether a formal hazard analysis system is needed. In the case of lower risk operations, inspections should aim to establish that adequate controls rather than a formal system are in operation.

64   In all cases, as stated in Section F, a commitment to proper management controls is vital for a hazard analysis system to be regarded as satisfactory.

65   Industry Guides to Good Hygiene Practice are expected to contain advice on these issues. **Authorised officers must give due consideration to Industry Guides and should have regard to any advice issued by Central Government Departments or by LACOTS.** (See Section K for general advice on enforcement of hazard analysis requirements.)

66   **In the first twelve months after coming into force of the Food Safety (General Food Hygiene) Regulations 1995, food businesses will need particular help and advice in adjusting to the new requirements.** Authorities are not normally expected to consider the service of an Improvement Notice or legal action in relation to enforcement of the requirements relating to hazard analysis in this period.

ii. Requirements for the Training and Supervision of Food Handlers

67   The requirements of the Food Safety (General Food Hygiene) Regulations 1995, relating to the supervision, instruction and/or training of food handlers, apply except where there are specific requirements for training in product-specific food hygiene regulations. More specific advice may be given on the latter in other Codes of Practice.

68   The level and content of training, instruction or supervision for food handlers is a responsibility placed on the food business to determine, having regard to the nature of the business and the role played by food handlers within it.

69   Training requirements should be assessed by food businesses as part of a hazard analysis system. **Where there is a satisfactory hazard analysis system, it should not be necessary for authorised officers to assess the effectiveness of training by discussion with staff, other than as confirmation of the discussion about the hazard analysis system with the food business proprietor or representative.** Guidance in the following paragraphs on the enforcement of training requirements applies in other circumstances.

Matters to be considered in assessing the level of training or instruction where a satisfactory hazard analysis system is not in place

70   **Any assessment of training levels should give due consideration to relevant UK or EC Industry Guides to Good**

Hygiene Practice. The guidance in paragraphs 72 to 75 applies particularly where there is no relevant UK or EC Industry Guide.

71 **In assessing whether the level and content of any training provided meets legal requirements, the food authority should consider the relative risk of operations, in the same way as for other aspects of the inspection.**

72 UK food hygiene and processing regulations do not define `food handler'. Existing guidance issued by the food industry suggests that the term should encompass factory operatives, shop assistants, catering staff and includes volunteers and staff recruited temporarily. In any initial assessment of needs for training, instruction, or supervision, a comprehensive definition should be used, encompassing any and all staff handling food in any form. The staff covered will, therefore, be very wide ranging in their needs for training, instruction, or supervision, eg, from those handling only packaged, ambient-stable foods, who may need only simple instruction on safety measures, to staff handling high risk, open foods who will usually need a form of structured training, which should be updated at intervals.

73 The level of training which a food authority can expect in respect of persons handling high risk open foods is the equivalent of training contained in the basic or certificate food hygiene course accredited by the CIEH, IEHO, REHIS, RSH, RIPHH, SOFHT and other similar training organisations. In-house training may be able to provide an equivalent level of training, even if the training is not accredited by such organisations. "Equivalent" in this context means equivalent in training standard—course content must also be appropriate.

74 **In assessing the level of training or instruction which should be expected of food businesses dealing with low risk foods, the food authority should recognise that in many cases the provision of suitable written or oral advice to a food handler and active supervision may be sufficient to satisfy legal requirements.**

75 Where businesses decide not to include an examination in their training programme, particularly for staff dealing with high risk foods, authorised officers may wish to assess the level of food hygiene awareness during their routine inspections. Where the authorised officer has identified food hygiene problems which lead him to have concerns over the level of food hygiene awareness, he should discuss them with the proprietor.

Advice to food proprietors on training

76   Some food businesses, particularly the smaller and independent businesses, may seek advice from the food authority on how to meet training requirements. Food authorities should try to be helpful in response to such requests. In the absence of relevant UK or EC Industry Guides, the food authority may wish to direct the proprietor to any of the recognised training organisations. In doing so the food authority should avoid showing favour to any particular organisation.

77   **In giving any advice or guidance on the training of food handlers, the food authority should not imply that any particular examination or course provided by any training organisation is a mandatory requirement.**

iii. Other Requirements

78   Food authorities should recognize that, while certain requirements of these Regulations impose minimum hygiene standards which apply to all relevant food businesses, many other requirements of these Regulations are explicitly related to risk, ie, they recognize by use of terms such as "where necessary" or "where appropriate" that certain requirements should not apply to all food businesses or operations, as they are not always necessary to achieve food safety. **Authorised officers should have regard to food businesses' own hazard analysis, where this has been properly carried out, in determining how the Regulations apply to food businesses.**

79   **In all cases, food authorities should have regard to the risk presented to the safety and wholesomeness of foodstuffs when assessing the way in which a food business should comply with that requirement. When determining the risk to the safety and wholesomeness of a food, authorised officers must have regard to the manner in which it is handled and packed, and any process to which the food is subjected before supply to the final consumer and the condition under which it is displayed.**

80   **Authorised officers must also give due consideration to any relevant UK or EC Industry Guide to Good Hygiene Practice in determining how the Regulations apply to food businesses and particularly when the terms "where appropriate" or "where necessary" are used in the Regulations.** UK or EC Industry Guides may be used voluntarily by food businesses as a guide to compliance with the Regulations or with the EC Food Hygiene Directive. This means that other means of achieving the safety requirements of the Regulations and the Directive may be acceptable, provided those safety requirements are actually met.

81   The Regulations in some cases allow for alternative materials to those specified to be used, providing that the food business operator "can satisfy the Food Authority" that the materials used are appropriate. This does not mean that businesses are required to apply to food authorities before using these materials, although some businesses may find it helpful and prudent and they may be encouraged to do so.

82   Where materials are used which would not normally satisfy the requirements, food businesses should be able to demonstrate the adequacy of alternative materials including their understanding of any risks associated with their use. **Authorised officers must give due consideration to any relevant UK or EC Industry Guide to Good Hygiene Practice in considering requests. They should also have regard to any hazard analysis carried out by the food business. Where a food business operator has satisfied an authorised officer that materials other than those specified in the Regulations are appropriate, having regard to the risk the material would present to the safety and wholesomeness of food, the food authority should confirm that fact in writing.** This will reduce the risk of different interpretations being given over time. Food authorities are encouraged to discuss their responses to such requests in local Food Liaison Groups and to communicate their policies on use of alternative materials to food businesses, although it is recognised that some experience of the operation of the Regulations may be needed before this is possible. See also Section I of this Code on coordination of advice and enforcement.

83   **Where there is no UK or EC Industry Guide relevant to the food business, food authorities should have regard to food businesses' own hazard analysis, where this has been properly carried out, in determining how the Regulations apply to food businesses.** Where there are no relevant Industry Guides, the following guidance may be helpful.

84   Chapters I to X of Schedule 1 to the Regulations provide basic food hygiene requirements, including design requirements, for food businesses. The application of the requirements, eg that in paragraph 3 of Chapter I for "adequate washbasins" and interpretation of requirements "where necessary" or "where appropriate", will vary according to the nature of the business, the nature of the food, and the risk associated with the way the food is handled. **In the absence of a relevant Industry Guide and where the business does not have a hazard analysis system, authorised officers may question the food business operator's awareness of risks in the business and should question any assumption that requirements for structures, equipment, and premises normally accepted in the trade do not apply to the business. Food authorities should**

have regard to paragraphs 46 and 47 in interpreting these requirements.

85   Requirements in Schedule 1, Chapter III for moveable, temporary, domestic, and other premises are nearly all qualified by the term "where necessary" and an overarching requirement related to practicability. Authorised officers should pay particular regard to the practicalities of requirements, especially where small scale or occasional operations are involved. The emphasis in this Chapter is on food handling practices which effectively prevent the contamination of food.

INSPECTION RATING—THE PRIORITY CLASSIFICATION OF FOOD PREMISES

1. *Basic Principles*

   1.1 All food premises should be subject to a detailed assessment based on the criteria detailed in this Annex.

   1.2 A form which illustrates the system, and is suitable for use when operating it, is at Annex 1(i). The officer should complete the form following a general inspection and update the score at any subsequent inspection.

   1.3 Officers should use the full range of scores available within this system as the purpose of the rating system will be frustrated by cautious marking or by a reluctance to recognise management/control systems.

   1.4 The operation of the inspection rating scheme should be subject to periodic management review to ensure that the scheme is being used correctly by staff and to discuss and amend their scoring criteria accordingly.

2. *Question 1: The Potential Hazard*

   2.1 The following three factors should be considered before determining the potential hazard of premises:

   2.2 (a) **Type of Food and Method of Handling**

   Type of food and degree to which food will be handled using the guidance below—Score 5-40.

   2.3 **Guidance on the Scoring System**

   Score

   5   Preparation of foods other than high risk by voluntary and charitable groups;

   Day-to-day retail handling of foods other than high risk, such as fruit, vegetables, canned and other ambient shelf stable products;

   10   Day-to-day handling of prepacked high risk foods; and preparation (including cooking) of high risk foods in establishments supplying less than 20 consumers each day;

wholesalers and distributors of shelf stable foods;

Premises which operate for 3 or less days per week, for example some village halls and community centres;

Premises involved in the filleting, salting or cold smoking of fish without subsequent modified atmosphere packaging.

30   Day-to-day handling or preparation (including cooking) of open high risk foods, for example supermarkets, restaurants, staff canteens, public houses, takeaways, sandwich preparation, delicatessens supplying more than 20 consumers each day;

Production/manufacture including packing of foods other than high risk;

Wholesalers of high risk foods;

Dispatch Centres—shellfish.

40   Production/manufacture of high risk foods such as cooked meat and poultry, dairy products;

Centres where shellfish are purified.

2.4   High risk foods may be regarded as those foods that support the growth of micro-organisms, and/or are intended for consumption without further treatment that could destroy pathogenic micro-organisms or their toxins.

2.5   (b) *Method of Processing*

An additional score of 20 should be included for certain food processes where the potential hazard is greater.

2.6   The following should be included in this category:

manufacture of cooked and chilled food (excluding catering establishments); ie cooked and prepared meals or foods which may be eaten cold or after reheating;

thermal processing of low-acid products;

aseptic packing of low-acid products;

vacuum packing including sous-vide but excluding raw and unprocessed meats and dried foods;

small-scale production of cooked meat products eg certain retailers including butchers;

small-scale production of dairy products;

purification of shellfish.

2.7 (c) *Consumers at Risk*

The officer should consider the number of *consumers* likely to be put at risk if there is a failure of food hygiene and safety procedures.

2.8 *Guidance on the Scoring System*
Score

0   Very Few—(this includes premises supplying less than 20 consumers each day);

5   Few—(this includes premises supplying essentially local trade, for example high street or corner shop, local restaurant);

10   Intermediate—(this category would include rather larger businesses whose trade extends outside of the town or district, for example hypermarket, small local manufacturer);

15   Substantial—(larger manufacturers whose products are distributed nationally or internationally);

2.9 An *additional score* to that above should also be included for catering premises where the consumers predominantly fall within a vulnerable group.

20   Premises serving vulnerable groups eg

(a) the elderly and children under five years, where there are more than 20 persons in the vulnerable group at risk, and

(b) the sick, the immuno-compromised.

3.   *Question 2: Level of (Current) Compliance*

3.1 The food hygiene and safety procedures and the structure of the premises should be assessed separately using the scoring system below:

(a) Food hygiene and safety includes food handling practices and procedures, temperature control;

(b) Structural includes cleanliness, layout, condition of structure, lighting, ventilation, facilities etc.

3.2 The officer should score the compliance observed during the inspection according to the guidance set out below. Adherence to any relevant UK or EC Industry Guide to Good Hygiene Practice should be considered when assessing compliance.

An appropriate level of conformity with relevant national guideline or industry codes of recommended practice will also be necessary to satisfy being categorised as 'Fair', 'Good' or 'Very good'.

3.3 *Guidance on the Scoring System*

Score

   0   Very good—high standard of compliance with statutory obligations and industry codes of recommended practice, conforms to accepted good practices in the trade;

   5   Good—high standard of compliance with statutory obligations and industry codes of recommended practice, some improvements still possible;

  10   Fair—some non-compliance with statutory obligations and industry codes of recommended practice. The premises are in the top 50 per cent of premises and standards are being maintained or improved;

  15   Poor—some non-compliance with statutory obligations —more effort required to prevent fall in standards;

  20   Bad—general failure to satisfy statutory obligations. Standards generally low;

  25   Very bad—almost total non-compliance with statutory obligations.

4. *Question 3: Confidence in Management/Control Systems*

4.1 Scope of the question—the performance of management will be scored in question 2 on the basis of the results achieved. A management with good food hygiene performance well understood by the workforce should have achieved a good standard in question 2 and hence a low score.

4.2 The question on confidence is not meant to consider this aspect again but to elicit a judgement from the inspector on the likelihood of the maintenance of satisfactory compliance in the future.

4.3 Several factors will influence the inspector's judgement including:

(a) the "track record" of the company, its willingness to act on previous advice and enforcement and the complaint history of the company;

(b) the attitude of the present management towards hygiene and food safety and the level of food hygiene training;

(c) the technical knowledge within or available to the company on hygiene and food safety matters; including hazard analysis and the control of critical points;

(d) the existence of external quality assurance accreditation, or satisfactory documented procedures and food safety management systems.

4.4 *Guidance on the Scoring System*

The scoring ranges from 0–30 (no confidence). A high score would boost the inspection rating and indicate the need for more frequent inspections.

Score

0   Highly Confident—good record of compliance. Access to technical advice within organisation. Subject to internal inspection. May have satisfactory Quality Assurance or food safety management system (including HACCP or similar systems).

5   Moderate Confidence—reasonable record of compliance. Technical advice available. Have satisfactory procedures and systems. Able to demonstrate appreciation of hazards.

10   Some Confidence—satisfactory record of compliance. Access to technical advice from trade associations. May have satisfactory food safety management system. Some appreciation of hazards.

20   Little Confidence—varying record of compliance. Little appreciation of hazards and quality control. No food safety management system.

30   No Confidence—poor track record of compliance. Little or no technical knowledge. No appreciation of hazards or quality control. No food safety management system.

INSPECTION RATING SCHEME

A PREMISES: NAME:
                    ADDRESS: _____

B DATE OF INSPECTION:
    INSPECTING OFFICER: _____

		TICK	SCORE

1.	*Potential Hazard*			
	(a)	*Type of Food and Method of Handling*		
		Handling low risk foods		5
		Handling high risk		10
		Preparation high risk		30
		Production high risk		40

	(b)	*Method of Processing*		
		High risk activities eg		
		Cooked and Chilled Foods		20
		Aseptic packing low acid food		
		Retail and small producers of cooked meats		
		Thermal processing, low acid foods		

	(c)	*Consumers at Risk*		
		Very few		0
		Few		5
		Intermediate		10
		Substantial		15
		*Vulnerable groups (catering)		20
		*(additional to score above)		

2.	*Compliance*			
	(a)	*Food Hygiene and Safety*	Very good	0
			Good	5
			Fair	10
			Poor	15
			Bad	20
			Very bad	25

	(b)	*Structural*	Very good	0
			Good	5
			Fair	10
			Poor	15
			Bad	20
			Very bad	25

3.	*Confidence in Management/Control Systems*		
		Highly confident	0
		Moderate confidence	5
		Some confidence	10
		Little confidence	20
		No confidence	30

INSPECTION RATING TOTAL:

INSPECTION RATING SCHEME

Category	Points Range	Max	Minimum Frequency of Inspection
A	91	— 175	(at least) every 6 months
B	71	— 90	(at least) every year
C	41	— 70	(at least) every 18 months
D	31	— 40	(at least) every 2 years
E	21	— 30	(at least) every 3 years
F	less than 21		(at least) every 5 years

INSPECTION OF FARMS AND PRIMARY PRODUCERS OF FOOD AND FOOD SOURCES

1   The Food Safety Act does not differentiate between primary producers of food and food sources (for example, farms, horticultural crop producers, bee-keepers, vineyards and fish farms) and other types of premises. Instead Section 1(3) sets out the following definitions:—

   — *food sources* means any growing crop or live animal, bird or fish from which food is intended to be derived;

   — *a food business* is a business in the course of which commercial operations with respect to food or food sources are carried out;

   — *food premises* are premises used for the purpose of a food business;

   — *commercial operations* in relation to a food source mean deriving food from it for the purpose of sale or for purposes connected with sale.

2   A food source becomes *food* once it has been harvested, gathered, slaughtered etc to be used for human consumption. Primary producers of *food* are running food businesses within the terms of the Act and it applies to them precisely as it applies to all other food businesses.

3   However, producers who handle only *food sources* (not food) and who do not carry out commercial operations in respect of them are *not* running food businesses within the terms of the Act. Examples include livestock farms or fish farms which sell only live animals or fish or nurseries selling only live plants.

4   The Act applies to *farm shops* precisely as it applies to other food shops.

Primary Producers Running Food Businesses

5   Food authorities should include premises used for food businesses in their regular inspection programmes. They should follow the guidance set out in this and other relevant Codes of Practice.

Primary Producers Not Running Food Businesses

6   Food authorities do *not* need to include premises which are not used for food businesses in their regular inspection programmes.

7   Authorised officers of food authorities do nevertheless have powers of entry to such premises under Section 32 of the Food Safety Act in order to enforce the Act and relevant regulations made under it (for example, regulations covering food sources). They may visit such premises, for example, in order to investigate a problem which has arisen further down the food chain.

REPORT OF A FOOD HYGIENE INSPECTION CARRIED OUT UNDER THE FOOD SAFETY ACT 1990

1   NAME AND ADDRESS OF PREMISES:

2   PERSON(S) SEEN/INTERVIEWED:

3   TYPE OF PREMISES:

4   DATE AND TIME OF INSPECTION:

5   AREAS INSPECTED: WHOLE OF PREMISES:
    PART OF PREMISES (please specify):

6   RECORDS EXAMINED:

7   DETAILS OF ANY SAMPLES PROCURED (eg description, batch number):

8   SUMMARY OF ACTION TO BE TAKEN BY THE AUTHORITY (eg follow-up letter, service of improvement or emergency prohibition notice):

THIS REPORT ONLY COVERS THE AREAS INSPECTED AT THE TIME OF THE INSPECTION. IT DOES NOT INDICATE COMPLIANCE WITH ANY PROVISION OF THE FOOD SAFETY ACT 1990 OR OF ANY REGULATIONS UNDER IT.

IT IS NOT A NOTICE REQUIRING WORKS TO BE CARRIED OUT.

SIGNED BY:
NAME IN BLOCK CAPITALS:
DESIGNATION:
AUTHORITY:
DATE:

Printed in the United Kingdom for HMSO
Dd 301205, C50, 8/95, 3400, 5673, 330555.